W9-BUW-128

After Dark

Creatures of the New Zealand Forest

Julia Crouth

SCHOLASTIC

AUCKLAND SYDNEY NEW YORK LONDON TORONTO
MEXICO CITY NEW DELHI HONG KONG

The symbol of the best
in children's literature
from Scholastic

For my sister Tania,
who guided my artistic endeavours
through childhood drawing lessons.

Love to you always.

First published in 2004 by Scholastic New Zealand Limited
Private Bag 94407, Greenmount, Auckland 1730, New Zealand

All rights reserved. No part of this publication may be
reproduced or transmitted in any form or by any means, electronic
or mechanical, including photocopying, recording, storage in any
information retrieval system, or otherwise,
without prior written permission of the publisher.

National Library of New Zealand Cataloguing-in-Publication Data

Crouth, Julia.
After dark : creatures of the NZ forest / Julia Crouth.
ISBN 1-86943-634-2
[1. Nocturnal animals-New Zealand-Fiction. 2. Forest animals-
New Zealand-Fiction.] I. Title.
NZ823.2-dc 22

9 8 7 6 5 4 3 2 1   4 5 6 7 8 9/ 0

Illustrations created using acrylic paints

Publishing team: Christine Dale, Penny Scown and Annette Bisman
Cover design and layout by Vasanti Unka
Typeset in 15/30 Optima Regular

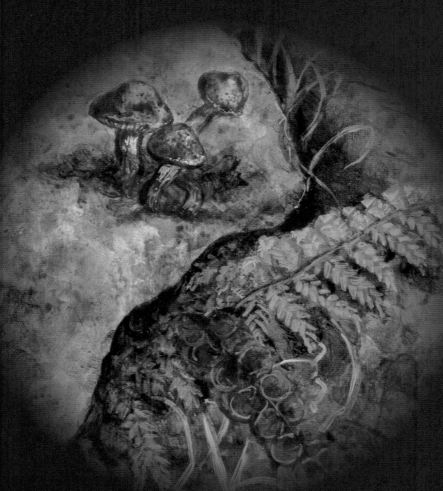

Our forests are a sight to be seen,

by daytime's warm clear light.

But when the sun sets and the light turns dim,

and colours are no longer bright . . .

strange noises are heard on the forest floor.

Eyes look down from the trees . . .

a grunt and a growl, a whistling call,

a snuffle, a sniff and a sneeze.

These noises are made by a night-hunting bird

that's searching for insects to eat.

It has brown shaggy feathers, tiny black eyes

and rather large legs and feet.

At night it relies on touch and smell,

with whiskers to feel around.

By day you'll find it fast asleep,

holed up in a nest on the ground.

With no wings to fly, or even a tail,

it's the strangest bird you'll see:

a pear-shaped body and a long, slender beak . . .

it's New Zealand's brown kiwi.

In the dark you can hear a hissing noise –
an angry insect is near.
A gecko has crossed this giant's path
and now runs away in fear.

This creature's body is covered in armour,
its legs have spikes and claws.
It has long antennae to feel for food
and very strong teeth and jaws.

This insect lives under bark and stones.
At night it comes out to eat.
Dead insects and fruit, plants and leaves,
all make a tasty treat.

Although it may look mean and scary,
it is really quite slow and tame.
It's New Zealand's largest insect . . .

giant weta is its name.

From down on the ground comes a curious sound,
a very faint, squeaking call.
This creature is looking for insects to eat.
It's secretive, swift and small.

With splashes of colour, brown, black and green,
its body is smooth and slim.
It has no webbing between its toes
and does not like to swim.

The female will lay her eggs on the ground
inside a damp stump or crack.
The male will guard them and when the eggs hatch
the babies will climb on his back!

In daytime they find a moist place to hide
beneath a stone or log.
This little creature is now endangered . . .

our tiny Archey's frog.

Gliding silently through the cool damp air
is a creature of the night,
with leathery wings and soft velvet fur
that's brown, speckled with white.

In hollow trees or in small burrows
it sleeps the day away,
then flies at night, using its sonar
to help it find its way.

It rolls up its wings when climbing
or crawling on the ground.
It rummages through the leaf litter
where food is often found.

It often sips nectar from flowers
or feasts on insects and fruit.
It's a native mammal with large pointed ears . . .

the short-tailed bat – how cute!

The old forest dragon wakes up from his sleep
and out of his burrow he crawls.
He's ready to feast on insects and worms.
With a loud croak, he calls.

This lizard may seek shelter with birds
but will eat chicks and eggs.
It has rough-scaled skin and sharp, pointed teeth,
a powerful jaw and legs.

Behind its two eyes is a scaly bump,
a third eye that cannot see.
When attacked it can drop off part of its tail,
which gives it a chance to flee.

When angry, it stiffens the spines on its back,
its skin is speckled like sand.
It can live to one hundred years or more . . .

the tuatara of New Zealand.

Something is stirring in the damp undergrowth –
at night it no longer hides.
It uncoils its body and stretches right out,
on one giant foot it glides.

Its large, gleaming shell is spiralled and striped
with ochre, brown or red.
It has rough, bumpy skin that's kept very moist
and tentacles on its head.

Its tongue is covered in thousands of teeth
like tiny, pointed nails.
It uses its tongue to devour its food –
insects, worms and snails.

This carnivorous hunter of the forest floor
slides on a sparkling trail.
This New Zealand giant is now hard to find . . .

the magnificent kauri snail.

Silently soaring through cool night air,
spotting movement at a glance,
this creature swoops down on a lurking rat,
which doesn't stand a chance.

Small birds and lizards, insects and rodents
are what this creature eats.
Yet when the sun begins to rise,
to a treetop it retreats.

It has sensitive eyes that are large and round
with pupils that expand at night.
It builds its nest in a hole in a tree
and its chicks hatch out all white.

Their feathers are soft, spotted and striped,
their beaks are hooked and small.
A familiar noise that is heard at night . . .

the morepork's whistling call.

From a crack in the bark of an old kowhai tree
crawls a creature with large round eyes.
Its skin is patterned like moss, bark and leaves –
it's wearing the perfect disguise.

If trapped and in danger, with no escape,
it's able to shed its tail.
It cannot blink as its eyes are covered
by one transparent scale.

With a lick from its tongue, it cleans its eyes,
its mouth is orange and bright.
It feasts on insects, nectar and fruit,
and changes colour from dark to light.

It can make many noises: a croak or a squeal
or a chirping, chattering echo.
It gives birth to live young and doesn't lay eggs . . .

it is the forest gecko.

From far away on this quiet, still night
a booming noise is heard –
the loud deep sound of a courtship call,
made by a very large bird.

The male digs out a bowl in the earth
and calls nightly for months on end.
Until he manages to find a mate,
these messages he will send.

This bird has wings but cannot fly
although it can climb trees.
It forages each night on the forest floor
for roots, fruit, berries and leaves.

A flightless parrot with an owl-like face
and features like no other bird.
How sad it would be to lose this treasure . . .

the kakapo – now rarely heard.

New Zealand has unique wildlife
found nowhere else on earth,
but if our environment is to survive,
we must realise its worth.

We've brought with us many predators
that kill our native life:
cats, rats, stoats and possums
are causing so much strife.

But imagine our land without any forests,
no animals or plants to see.
If we don't help to protect them now,
think how empty our world would be.

About Julia Grouth

Julia has been illustrating children's books since 1999. Most have been for educational reading programmes. *After Dark* is her second picture book for general sale.

Of her work, Julia says, "I have always been passionate about animals and nature. Growing up, I wanted to work with animals as a career. I grew up on a farm and worked part-time at my dad's horse stables, whilst illustrating books. Through my books I can share this passion with children, so they can appreciate and learn about some of the amazing creatures we have on this planet.

"Being a New Zealander, I have a special interest in our wildlife and hope to do my part in making sure these treasures remain in our forest."

Julia lives in Pukekohe and is currently training to be a teacher of art and design.